# Monet's House and Garden Diary 1999

# MONET'S HOUSE & GARDEN

## Diary 1999

Heide Michels
Guy Bouchet
Translation by Helen Ivor

FRANCES LINCOLN

Frances Lincoln Limited
4 Torriano Mews
Torriano Avenue
London NW5 2RZ

Monet's House and Garden Diary 1999

British Library cataloguing-in-publication data
A catalogue record for this book is available from the British Library

ISBN 0-7112-1258-9

Printed in Hong Kong

First Frances Lincoln edition 1998

*Front cover* A Normandy dresser in the dining room.

*Page 1* Poppies and other flowers flourished in the gardens and
countryside around Giverny, furnishing Monet with
subjects for many compositions.

*Pages 2-3* Monet's house at Giverny in the Seine valley was a
modest building, with a slate roof and a long plain façade
rendered in pink, unlike the others in the village. A row of
windows along one side faced south and looked out on to a
little orchard, with the river beyond.

*Page 5* The dining room, as visitors would have seen it when
entering the hall.

*Back cover* The entrance to Monet's house.

# Introduction

Few painters have come to be so closely identified with
their homes as Claude Monet is with Giverny.

In 1883 he set up home there with Alice Hoschedé
whom he married in 1892, her six children and his
two children. He began the transformation of the
neglected orchard and potager into a flower garden
almost the minute he moved in, so there would be
plenty of subjects to paint. Initially he did the planting
and tending himself, with some help from the children.

He made improvements to the house gradually.
The layout stayed roughly the same, with double doors
leading from the garden to a central hall from which
interconnecting rooms led one into another on either
side. He extended and modernized the kitchen at one
end and added a room at the other by converting the
barn into a studio drawing room, with a short flight of
steps connecting it to the house.

Monet employed no interior designers but relied
instead on craftsmen who followed his plans. He chose
traditional local materials, such as wall tiles from Rouen
and Normandy furniture, to which he added touches of
eastern exoticism, such as a colourful rug on the floor
of the studio drawing room. His sensitivity to light and
colour infused the interior, boldly but simply decorated
to provide a perfect backdrop to family life and a
harmonious place to entertain friends.

In 1893 Monet bought a strip of land at the lower
end of the garden, where he created an extensive water
garden. He spent hours by the waterlily pond,
contemplating the play of light on water. During the
forty-three years he spent at Giverny, the water garden
and flower garden, and the surrounding countryside,
inspired much of his greatest work.

# December 1998 & January 1999

---

28 Monday

---

29 Tuesday

---

30 Wednesday

---

Monet's studio drawing room doubled as a place for working as well as for entertaining. Comfortable seating was arranged round the perimeter of the room so as to leave space in the middle from which to view the rows of canvases on the walls. The studio gradually became a gallery for Monet's past work, and for many visitors it was as much a source of interest as the celebrated gardens. In this photograph of 1913 the artist stands in the middle of the room, smoking the inevitable 'Caporal rose' cigarette.

31 Thursday

---

1 Friday

*New Year's Day*
*Holiday, UK, Republic of Ireland, Canada,*
*USA, Australia and New Zealand*

---

2 Saturday          *Full Moon*

---

3 Sunday

---

# January 1999

4 Monday

5 Tuesday

6 Wednesday                                                          *Epiphany*

7 Thursday

When the painter was not
working, the studio
drawing room became a
setting for family activities.
Both Monet and his wife,
Alice, were keen on
reading, and in the winter,
when there were not so
many visitors, they enjoyed
the works of Tolstoy and
Ibsen as well as the novels
of French writers such as
Balzac and Flaubert. When,
after Alice's death, her
daughter Blanche took over
her role as companion and
housekeeper, she would
often relax after dinner here
over a game of backgammon
with her stepfather.

8 Friday

9 Saturday          *Last Quarter*

10 Sunday

# January 1999

11  Monday

12  Tuesday

13  Wednesday

14  Thursday

15  Friday

16  Saturday

17  Sunday          *New Moon*

The waterlily pond, with a little green Japanese bridge across it, inspired Monet's waterlily paintings and his most ambitious project, the large-scale panels called the *Grandes Décorations des Nymphéas*. They remain the most eloquent testimony to Giverny and its creator.

# January 1999

18 Monday

19 Tuesday

20 Wednesday

21 Thursday

22 Friday

23 Saturday

24 Sunday *First Quarter*

In the studio drawing room, family photographs and the latest art journals sent from Paris jostled for space with finely glazed ceramic pots filled with vibrant flowers from the garden.

# January 1999

25 Monday

26 Tuesday                                    *Holiday, Australia (Australia Day)*

27 Wednesday

28 Thursday

The focal point of the
kitchen was the large
cooking range. Fuelled by
wood or coal, it was placed
between the window and
fireplace so that fumes
could be directed out of the
room. It had hot plates
whose temperature could
be adjusted, a plate warmer
and two ovens. The cook
and her helpers could
prepare sauces and meat
or fish dishes, steam
vegetables and bake cakes
all at the same time.

29 Friday

30 Saturday

31 Sunday          *Full Moon*

# February 1999

1   Monday

2   Tuesday

3   Wednesday

4   Thursday

5   Friday

6   Saturday                                    *Holiday, New Zealand (Waitangi Day)*

7   Sunday

Monet had a collection of 231 Japanese prints, such as these two by Hiroshige in the dining room. He became fascinated with the skilful way Japanese artists reproduced their world through a combination of colour and line.

# February 1999

8 Monday *Last Quarter*

9 Tuesday

10 Wednesday

11 Thursday

12 Friday *Holiday, USA (Lincoln's birthday)*

13 Saturday

14 Sunday *St Valentine's Day*

Monet's bold scheme for the dining room – light chrome yellow for the walls, with cornices, dado and door frames picked out in a brighter yellow – was repeated in the furniture. The family collection of blue and white china echoed the Rouen tiles of the fire surround.

# February 1999

---

15 Monday

---

16 Tuesday     *New Moon*
*Shrove Tuesday*

---

17 Wednesday
*Ash Wednesday*

---

18 Thursday

---

19 Friday

---

20 Saturday

---

21 Sunday

---

Monet would spend hours seated on his bench contemplating the beauties of his water garden, his private world of shadow and reflection. His waterlily paintings became increasingly abstract: recognizable landmarks such as the river bank or the bridge in the background were gradually abandoned so that all that was left was the play of light and reflection on the surface of the water.

# February 1999

22 Monday

23 Tuesday        *First Quarter*

24 Wednesday

25 Thursday

26 Friday

27 Saturday

28 Sunday

In Monet's bedroom, the bed, with fluted corner posts and moulded headboard, had fine linen sheets embroidered with his initials and pillowcases edged in lace.

# March 1999

1   Monday

2   Tuesday        *Full Moon*

3   Wednesday

4   Thursday

5   Friday

6   Saturday

7   Sunday

Monet's largest studio at Giverny was a twentieth-century construction of iron trusses, concrete and glass, built so that he could work on the large-scale decorative panels that were to be the culmination of his career. The two sofas were placed back to back in the centre, for Monet and his guests to view his work in comfort; the only other furnishings were some occasional chairs, easels and the tables on which he kept his equipment.

# March 1999

8  Monday

9  Tuesday

10  Wednesday        *Last Quarter*

11  Thursday

12  Friday

13  Saturday

14  Sunday        *Mothering Sunday*

Monet used pastels intermittently throughout his career, often while he was away on painting trips waiting for his canvases to arrive, and sometimes as a simple change from oils.

# March 1999

15 Monday

16 Tuesday

17 Wednesday        *New Moon*                    *Holiday, Northern Ireland and Republic of Ireland*

18 Thursday

19 Friday

20 Saturday

21 Sunday

The critic Arsène Alexandre described the 'stretch of water' that was Monet's water garden as 'a masterpiece by some goldsmith who has blended together alloys of the most magic metals'. Monet surrounded it with weeping willows and poplars, rare lilies, azaleas, rhododendrons and roses, and trained white and mauve wisterias over the bridge.

# March 1999

22  Monday

23  Tuesday

24  Wednesday          *First Quarter*

25  Thursday

26  Friday

27  Saturday

28  Sunday

*Palm Sunday*
*British Summer Time begins*
*(subject to confirmation)*

The blue salon, an essentially feminine room, was the setting for family activities. Here Monet, Alice and the children gathered to read and sew, play card games or listen to music. For the painter, it was primarily a library, where he kept his large collection of books on botany.

# March & April 1999

29 Monday

30 Tuesday

31 Wednesday    *Full Moon*

1  Thursday    *Passover (Pesach) First Day*

In fine weather the garden became the setting for the family's mealtime rituals. Afternoon tea was a full-scale ceremony. A table would be laid outside with delicate Creil china on a white embroidered table-cloth, finely worked napkins, small silver spoons and a china teapot, or one in pewter. A range of delicious delicacies would be served, all home-made by Marguerite, Monet's favourite cook.

2  Friday    *Good Friday*

3  Saturday

4  Sunday    *Easter Sunday*

# April 1999

Week 14

5   Monday

*Easter Monday*
*Holiday, UK (exc.Scotland), Republic of Ireland,*
*Canada, Australia and New Zealand*

6   Tuesday

7   Wednesday

8   Thursday

The épicerie served as a cloakroom or lobby, as well as a store for flavourings and exotic spices, dry goods and table linen. The Monet household's love of the outdoor life was evident in the hats that festooned the bamboo stand. The stand's central mirror reflected the sideboard on which stood earthenware jugs and tall stoneware jars full of intensely flavoured oil from Provence.

9   Friday      *Last Quarter*

10  Saturday

11  Sunday

# April 1999

12  Monday

13  Tuesday

14  Wednesday

15  Thursday

16  Friday          *New Moon*

17  Saturday                                        *Islamic New Year (subject to sighting of moon)*

18  Sunday

The hall is the culminating point of the Grande Allée, the main north-south axis running through the flower garden. Looking through the hall's double doors, visitors would have seen banks of flower beds, planted so that there was a succession of colourful blooms from the beginning of spring through to the first frosts of winter.

# April 1999

19 Monday

20 Tuesday

21 Wednesday                                          *Birthday of Queen Elizabeth II*

Alice used beauty products
based on light fragrances
which were often named
after the flowers from which
they were made, such as
orange-flower water from
Grasse, powders scented
with Alpine violets, bath oil
with tuberose, and white
lavender spirit for massaging
the skin. Cut-glass bottles
and soap dishes, a nail
buffer, a tortoiseshell comb
edged with silver, a
swansdown powder puff
and tortoiseshell combs for
securing a chignon were all
essential to her toilette.

22 Thursday          *First Quarter*

23 Friday

24 Saturday

25 Sunday                                          *Holiday, Australia and New Zealand (Anzac Day)*

# April & May 1999

26 Monday

27 Tuesday

28 Wednesday

29 Thursday

30 Friday          *Full Moon*

1  Saturday

2  Sunday

When the studio drawing room was converted from a high-ceilinged outbuilding adjoining one side of the house, large windows were cut into the walls to give views of the garden and the main entrance.

# May 1999

3 Monday

*May Day Holiday, UK (exc. Scotland) and Republic of Ireland*
*Spring Holiday, Scotland*

4 Tuesday

5 Wednesday

6 Thursday

7 Friday

8 Saturday *Last Quarter*

9 Sunday *Mother's Day, Canada and USA*

One of the early improvements Monet made to his house was the construction of a balcony which ran almost the entire length of the south façade. In the summer the balcony became a place for entertaining, where everyone could enjoy the visual splendours and perfumes of the garden.

# May 1999

10 Monday

11 Tuesday

12 Wednesday

13 Thursday                                          *Ascension Day*

14 Friday

15 Saturday        *New Moon*

16 Sunday

Monet believed that a beautiful dinner service was one of the keys to a successful meal. When important guests were expected, Alice brought out a white porcelain dinner service with wide yellow rims and a border of blue. Monet commissioned this service from the Cristallerie Royale de Champagne, to be made according to his own design.

# May 1999

17 Monday

18 Tuesday

19 Wednesday

20 Thursday

21 Friday                                                    *Jewish Feast of Weeks (Shavuot)*

22 Saturday          *First Quarter*

23 Sunday                                                    *Whit Sunday (Pentecost)*

In 1920 Monet removed the cypresses lining the Grande Allée, replacing them with flower beds and metal arches to support his favourite roses, planted in abundance: 'Everywhere you turn,' wrote Arsène Alexandre, ' – around your feet, above your head, at chest level – there are lakes, garlands and hedges of flowers, whose colour harmonies are at once improvised, yet calculated, and which renew themselves each season.'

# May 1999

Week 21

24 Monday

25 Tuesday

26 Wednesday

27 Thursday

28 Friday

29 Saturday

30 Sunday          *Full Moon*

As the two doors leading into the blue salon were not directly opposite each other, the sense of the long sweep of rooms on the ground floor was maintained by this beautifully ornate, strategically placed mirror. Its frame was painted the same pale blue as the walls, with a deeper version highlighting details.

# May & June 1999

31 Monday

1 Tuesday

2 Wednesday

3 Thursday

4 Friday

5 Saturday

6 Sunday

Alice's keepsakes form a picture of a devoted mother and wife and a lover of beautiful things. Among her collection of decorative watch cases were several engraved with the letter H for Hoschedé, her previous name.

# June 1999

7  Monday        *Last Quarter*                                    *Holiday, Republic of Ireland*
                                                            *Holiday, New Zealand (Queen's birthday)*

8  Tuesday

9  Wednesday

10 Thursday

11 Friday

12 Saturday                                   *The Queen's official birthday (subject to confirmation)*

13 Sunday        *New Moon*

A standard rose rising dramatically from a bed of irises and foxgloves. Monet's garden provided him with a kind of spiritual refuge. He was in the habit of strolling around it several times a day, checking on the progress of the plants and making sure that the gardeners were carrying out his detailed instructions.

14  Monday

15  Tuesday

16  Wednesday

17  Thursday

18  Friday

19  Saturday

20  Sunday          *First Quarter*                                    *Father's Day, UK, Canada and USA*

One of the desks in the studio drawing room, with a posy of Monet's favourite yellow 'Mermaid' roses. He was a prolific correspondent, maintaining contact with a wide circle of writers and painters, including Mallarmé, Boudin, Renoir and Sisley.

21 Monday

22 Tuesday

23 Wednesday

24 Thursday

25 Friday

26 Saturday

27 Sunday

On the balcony, free-standing trellises supported fragrant roses, amongst them the pale pink *Rosa* 'Albertine'.

28 Monday          *Full Moon*

29 Tuesday

30 Wednesday

1 Thursday          *Holiday, Canada (Canada Day)*

2 Friday

3 Saturday

4 Sunday          *Independence Day, USA*

According to Octave Mirbeau, Monet first came across Japanese prints while he was staying in Holland in 1871. Intrigued to find that his purchases from a grocer's shop were wrapped in a special paper printed with images of great beauty, depicting scenes of life in Japan, he went back to acquire the whole pile of prints that the grocer was using for packaging. These two, dating from around the mid-nineteenth century, are by Hiroshige.

# July 1999

Week 27

5 Monday

*Holiday, USA (observed)*

6 Tuesday  *Last Quarter*

7 Wednesday

8 Thursday

9 Friday

10 Saturday

11 Sunday

Like his paintings, Monet's garden was a profusion of colour, the crowding together of the flowers – as in this bed of *Rosa* 'François Juranville', sweet rocket and poppies – giving it its character.

# July 1999

12  Monday

13  Tuesday        *New Moon*

14  Wednesday

15  Thursday

16  Friday

With Alice's son Jean-Pierre, a keen botanist, Monet compiled a herbarium of dried petals and unusual plants. Monet also had a large collection of botanical reference works, which he would consult before sketching out planting schemes for his flower beds or drafting plans for the garden.

17  Saturday

18  Sunday

# July 1999

19  Monday

20  Tuesday  *First Quarter*

21  Wednesday

22  Thursday

23  Friday

24  Saturday

25  Sunday

*Robinia pseudoacacia* 'Frisia',
with hostas, geraniums
and a weeping willow in the
background, growing by the
poolside, provided a perfect
frame for the expanse of
water that became Monet's
chief subject.

26  Monday

27  Tuesday

28  Wednesday        *Full Moon*

29  Thursday

30  Friday

In the dining room the
glass-fronted dressers that
housed the Creil faience
used for everyday meals
were typical early
nineteenth-century pieces
from the Caux region of
Normandy. The cornices
were surmounted by
basket-handle arches with
double scrolls.

31  Saturday

1   Sunday

# August 1999

2 Monday

3 Tuesday

4 Wednesday    *Last Quarter*

5 Thursday

6 Friday

7 Saturday

8 Sunday

In its unadorned simplicity, Alice's bedroom was a far cry from a conventional nineteenth-century woman's boudoir, and seems to have been planned as a place to which Alice could withdraw from the bustle of the household for moments of contemplation on her own. It was here that she dealt with the practicalities of running the household, wrote letters and confided her private confessions to her diary.

# August 1999

9   Monday

10  Tuesday

11  Wednesday        *New Moon*

12  Thursday

13  Friday

14  Saturday

In late summer, trailing
nasturtiums carpeted the
Grande Allée. In the far
distance, beyond the garden
gate, Monet made his water
garden.

15  Sunday

# August 1999

16 Monday

17 Tuesday

18 Wednesday

19 Thursday     *First Quarter*

20 Friday

21 Saturday

22 Sunday

As a demanding gourmet, Monet took a keen interest in everything that happened in his kitchen. He was particularly fond of seafood – prawns with garlic and turbot served with a Hollandaise sauce.

# August 1999

23 Monday

24 Tuesday

25 Wednesday

26 Thursday          *Full Moon*

27 Friday

'In his garden amongst the flowers,' wrote Alexandre of Monet, 'he is filled with happiness.' Anyone who came to lunch would be conducted around the flower beds, water garden and greenhouses afterwards. Those who admired particular fruits and flowers often found that Monet sent them later as gifts.

28 Saturday

29 Sunday

# August & September 1999

Week 35

30 Monday

*Summer Holiday, UK (exc. Scotland)*

31 Tuesday

1 Wednesday

2 Thursday        *Last Quarter*

3 Friday

4 Saturday

5 Sunday

In Alice's bedroom, the sea-green walls were enlivened by pastel-blue paintwork on the doors, windows and mirror frame above the mantelpiece, on which stood two late-nineteenth-century Saxony faience candlesticks.

# September 1999

6 Monday

7 Tuesday

8 Wednesday

9 Thursday  *New Moon*

10 Friday

11 Saturday  *Jewish New Year (Rosh Hashanah)*

12 Sunday

The Louis XVI mirror frame over the marble mantelpiece in Monet's bedroom was decorated with strips of ovoli moulding, loosely knotted bows of carved ribbon and garlands of laurel leaves intertwined with fruit and flowers.

# September 1999

13 Monday

14 Tuesday

15 Wednesday

16 Thursday

17 Friday          *First Quarter*

18 Saturday

19 Sunday

After he acquired an additional piece of land at the other end of the village in 1890, Monet was able to cultivate his own soft fruit, herbs and vegetables. He visited the kitchen garden every day to make a personal selection of the fruit and vegetables, which were then conveyed to the kitchen.

# September 1999

20 Monday                                    *Jewish Day of Atonement (Yom Kippur)*

21 Tuesday

22 Wednesday

23 Thursday

24 Friday

25 Saturday          *Full Moon*          *Jewish Festival of Tabernacles (Succoth) First Day*

26 Sunday

The kitchen was decorated in shades of blue; the blue and white Rouen tiles covering the walls formed sparkling surfaces that were easy to clean. Vegetables from the kitchen garden were washed in the flat stone sink, and were often steamed, as Monet favoured this method of cooking.

# September & October 1999

27 Monday

28 Tuesday

29 Wednesday

30 Thursday

1   Friday

2   Saturday          *Last Quarter*

3   Sunday

In warm weather furniture from the studio drawing room was brought out on to the balcony. When it was time for aperitifs, visitors would be offered sparkling water, iced orangeade, cherry liqueur, a small port or a finger of scotch.

# October 1999

Week 40

---

4   Monday

---

5   Tuesday

---

6   Wednesday

---

7   Thursday

---

8   Friday

---

9   Saturday          *New Moon*

---

10  Sunday

---

When Monet first moved to Giverny his house was known as the Maison du Pressoir, after the cider presses of the neighbourhood, and cider was probably once made in the cellar. A number of varieties of apple were grown in the garden – some for making cider, some for eating, some for cooking.

# October 1999

---

11 Monday
*Holiday, Canada (Thanksgiving Day) and USA (Columbus Day)*

---

12 Tuesday

---

13 Wednesday

---

14 Thursday

---

15 Friday

---

16 Saturday

---

17 Sunday          *First Quarter*

---

The cellar, with its floor of beaten earth, served as a store for fruit and garden equipment. Pears and apples were stored on slatted racks with enough space between them to prevent any rot spreading.

# October 1999

18 Monday

19 Tuesday

20 Wednesday

21 Thursday

22 Friday

23 Saturday

24 Sunday          *Full Moon*

Monet would set up his easel beside the pond to capture a world of shadow and reflection.

# October 1999

---

25 Monday

*Holiday, Republic of Ireland*
*Holiday, New Zealand (Labour Day)*

---

26 Tuesday

---

27 Wednesday

---

28 Thursday

---

29 Friday

---

30 Saturday

---

31 Sunday          *Last Quarter*                    *British Summer Time ends*
                                                     *(subject to confirmation)*

---

In her bedroom Alice kept an invitation to the wedding of her daughter Marthe to the artist Theodore Butler, on 31 October 1900 at the church in Giverny. The couple married a year after Theodore was widowed by the death of Suzanne, Marthe's sister.

Monsieur et Madame
Claude Monet ont l'honneur
de vous faire part du Mariage
de Mademoiselle Marthe
Hoschedé, leur belle-fille et
fille, avec Monsieur Théodore
Earl Butler,

Et vous prient d'assister à la
Bénédiction Nuptiale qui leur sera
donnée le Lundi 31 Octobre 1900, à
11 heures 1/2 en l'Eglise de Giverny.

Giverny, par Vernon (Eure)

# November 1999

1   Monday

2   Tuesday

3   Wednesday

4   Thursday

5   Friday

6   Saturday

After lunch Monet would
retire to the studio drawing
room to enjoy a quiet coffee
and home-made fruit
brandies.

7   Sunday

# November 1999

---

8   Monday        *New Moon*




---

9   Tuesday




---

10  Wednesday




---

11  Thursday                    *Holiday, Canada (Remembrance Day) and USA*
                                              *(Veterans' Day)*




---

12  Friday




---

13  Saturday




---

14  Sunday                               *Remembrance Sunday*




---

In the late summer splendour of the long flower beds on the west side of the garden, running parallel to the Grande Allée, sunflowers, dahlias and Michaelmas daisies made a riot of yellows and mauves.

15 Monday

16 Tuesday     *First Quarter*

17 Wednesday

18 Thursday

For his correspondence, Monet used broad goose quill pens, which he cut himself. The roll-top desk in his bedroom also contained a travelling inkwell with a Japanese-style decoration, a finely chased silver pen holder and a dark green marble ashtray. In the many drawers Monet kept his private and business letters, financial papers and journals containing reviews of his exhibitions.

19 Friday

20 Saturday

21 Sunday

# November 1999

22  Monday

23  Tuesday                    *Full Moon*

24  Wednesday

25  Thursday                                        *Holiday, USA (Thanksgiving Day)*

26  Friday

27  Saturday

28  Sunday                                          *Advent Sunday*

The Monets' blue and
white Creil faience had a
delicate Japanese-inspired
decoration of cherry
blossom and little fans.

# November & December 1999

29 Monday *Last Quarter*

30 Tuesday

1 Wednesday

2 Thursday

3 Friday

4 Saturday *Jewish Festival of Chanukah, First Day*

5 Sunday

The huge Louis XVI mirror in Monet's bedroom, surmounting an imposing fireplace of white marble veined in grey, was placed partly to reflect the light from the windows and partly to create a sense of perspective and balance.

---

6   Monday

---

7   Tuesday          *New Moon*

---

8   Wednesday

---

9   Thursday                                          *Ramadān begins (subject to sighting of moon)*

---

10  Friday

---

11  Saturday

---

12  Sunday

Amongst the paraphernalia of equipment needed to bottle the home-made wine produced in Giverny's cellar there were copper funnels, corks and empty bottles.

13  Monday

14  Tuesday

15  Wednesday

16  Thursday        *First Quarter*

17  Friday

18  Saturday

19  Sunday

With so many meals to prepare, the kitchen was a hive of activity throughout the day and Monet's cook required a large amount of cooking pots, all kept scoured and gleaming, and within easy reach.

# December 1999

20 Monday

21 Tuesday

22 Wednesday        *Full Moon*

23 Thursday

24 Friday                                          *Christmas Eve*
                                          *Holiday, USA (observed)*

25 Saturday                                        *Christmas Day*

After meals, the usual custom was to retire to the studio drawing room for coffee, accompanied by small squares of fruit jelly flavoured with local raspberries, blackcurrants and bilberries.

26 Sunday                                          *Boxing Day*
                                          *St Stephen's Day*

# December 1999 & January 2000

Week 52

27 Monday                                      *Holiday, UK, Republic of Ireland, Canada, Australia*
                                                                          *and New Zealand*

28 Tuesday                                     *Holiday, UK, Republic of Ireland, Canada, Australia*
                                                                          *and New Zealand*

29 Wednesday        *Last Quarter*

30 Thursday

31 Friday                                                         *Millennium Holiday, UK*
                                                                      *(to be confirmed)*

1 Saturday                                                               *New Year's Day*

2 Sunday

Every morning before
Monet began painting,
the gardener would tend
the waterlilies from a boat,
cleaning leaves from the
surface of the pond.

# 1998

## JANUARY
| M | T | W | T | F | S | S |
|---|---|---|---|---|---|---|
|   |   |   | 1 | 2 | 3 | 4 |
| 5 | 6 | 7 | 8 | 9 | 10 | 11 |
| 12 | 13 | 14 | 15 | 16 | 17 | 18 |
| 19 | 20 | 21 | 22 | 23 | 24 | 25 |
| 26 | 27 | 28 | 29 | 30 | 31 |   |

## FEBRUARY
| M | T | W | T | F | S | S |
|---|---|---|---|---|---|---|
|   |   |   |   |   |   | 1 |
| 2 | 3 | 4 | 5 | 6 | 7 | 8 |
| 9 | 10 | 11 | 12 | 13 | 14 | 15 |
| 16 | 17 | 18 | 19 | 20 | 21 | 22 |
| 23 | 24 | 25 | 26 | 27 | 28 |   |

## MARCH
| M | T | W | T | F | S | S |
|---|---|---|---|---|---|---|
|   |   |   |   |   |   | 1 |
| 2 | 3 | 4 | 5 | 6 | 7 | 8 |
| 9 | 10 | 11 | 12 | 13 | 14 | 15 |
| 16 | 17 | 18 | 19 | 20 | 21 | 22 |
| 23 | 24 | 25 | 26 | 27 | 28 | 29 |
| 30 | 31 |   |   |   |   |   |

## APRIL
| M | T | W | T | F | S | S |
|---|---|---|---|---|---|---|
|   |   | 1 | 2 | 3 | 4 | 5 |
| 6 | 7 | 8 | 9 | 10 | 11 | 12 |
| 13 | 14 | 15 | 16 | 17 | 18 | 19 |
| 20 | 21 | 22 | 23 | 24 | 25 | 26 |
| 27 | 28 | 29 | 30 |   |   |   |

## MAY
| M | T | W | T | F | S | S |
|---|---|---|---|---|---|---|
|   |   |   |   | 1 | 2 | 3 |
| 4 | 5 | 6 | 7 | 8 | 9 | 10 |
| 11 | 12 | 13 | 14 | 15 | 16 | 17 |
| 18 | 19 | 20 | 21 | 22 | 23 | 24 |
| 25 | 26 | 27 | 28 | 29 | 30 | 31 |

## JUNE
| M | T | W | T | F | S | S |
|---|---|---|---|---|---|---|
| 1 | 2 | 3 | 4 | 5 | 6 | 7 |
| 8 | 9 | 10 | 11 | 12 | 13 | 14 |
| 15 | 16 | 17 | 18 | 19 | 20 | 21 |
| 22 | 23 | 24 | 25 | 26 | 27 | 28 |
| 29 | 30 |   |   |   |   |   |

## JULY
| M | T | W | T | F | S | S |
|---|---|---|---|---|---|---|
|   |   | 1 | 2 | 3 | 4 | 5 |
| 6 | 7 | 8 | 9 | 10 | 11 | 12 |
| 13 | 14 | 15 | 16 | 17 | 18 | 19 |
| 20 | 21 | 22 | 23 | 24 | 25 | 26 |
| 27 | 28 | 29 | 30 | 31 |   |   |

## AUGUST
| M | T | W | T | F | S | S |
|---|---|---|---|---|---|---|
|   |   |   |   |   | 1 | 2 |
| 3 | 4 | 5 | 6 | 7 | 8 | 9 |
| 10 | 11 | 12 | 13 | 14 | 15 | 16 |
| 17 | 18 | 19 | 20 | 21 | 22 | 23 |
| 24 | 25 | 26 | 27 | 28 | 29 | 30 |
| 31 |   |   |   |   |   |   |

## SEPTEMBER
| M | T | W | T | F | S | S |
|---|---|---|---|---|---|---|
|   | 1 | 2 | 3 | 4 | 5 | 6 |
| 7 | 8 | 9 | 10 | 11 | 12 | 13 |
| 14 | 15 | 16 | 17 | 18 | 19 | 20 |
| 21 | 22 | 23 | 24 | 25 | 26 | 27 |
| 28 | 29 | 30 |   |   |   |   |

## OCTOBER
| M | T | W | T | F | S | S |
|---|---|---|---|---|---|---|
|   |   |   | 1 | 2 | 3 | 4 |
| 5 | 6 | 7 | 8 | 9 | 10 | 11 |
| 12 | 13 | 14 | 15 | 16 | 17 | 18 |
| 19 | 20 | 21 | 22 | 23 | 24 | 25 |
| 26 | 27 | 28 | 29 | 30 | 31 |   |

## NOVEMBER
| M | T | W | T | F | S | S |
|---|---|---|---|---|---|---|
|   |   |   |   |   |   | 1 |
| 2 | 3 | 4 | 5 | 6 | 7 | 8 |
| 9 | 10 | 11 | 12 | 13 | 14 | 15 |
| 16 | 17 | 18 | 19 | 20 | 21 | 22 |
| 23 | 24 | 25 | 26 | 27 | 28 | 29 |
| 30 |   |   |   |   |   |   |

## DECEMBER
| M | T | W | T | F | S | S |
|---|---|---|---|---|---|---|
| 1 | 2 | 3 | 4 | 5 | 6 |
| 7 | 8 | 9 | 10 | 11 | 12 | 13 |
| 14 | 15 | 16 | 17 | 18 | 19 | 20 |
| 21 | 22 | 23 | 24 | 25 | 26 | 27 |
| 28 | 29 | 30 | 31 |   |   |   |

# 1999

## JANUARY
| M | T | W | T | F | S | S |
|---|---|---|---|---|---|---|
|   |   |   |   | 1 | 2 | 3 |
| 4 | 5 | 6 | 7 | 8 | 9 | 10 |
| 11 | 12 | 13 | 14 | 15 | 16 | 17 |
| 18 | 19 | 20 | 21 | 22 | 23 | 24 |
| 25 | 26 | 27 | 28 | 29 | 30 | 31 |

## FEBRUARY
| M | T | W | T | F | S | S |
|---|---|---|---|---|---|---|
| 1 | 2 | 3 | 4 | 5 | 6 | 7 |
| 8 | 9 | 10 | 11 | 12 | 13 | 14 |
| 15 | 16 | 17 | 18 | 19 | 20 | 21 |
| 22 | 23 | 24 | 25 | 26 | 27 | 28 |

## MARCH
| M | T | W | T | F | S | S |
|---|---|---|---|---|---|---|
| 1 | 2 | 3 | 4 | 5 | 6 | 7 |
| 8 | 9 | 10 | 11 | 12 | 13 | 14 |
| 15 | 16 | 17 | 18 | 19 | 20 | 21 |
| 22 | 23 | 24 | 25 | 26 | 27 | 28 |
| 29 | 30 | 31 |   |   |   |   |

## APRIL
| M | T | W | T | F | S | S |
|---|---|---|---|---|---|---|
|   |   |   | 1 | 2 | 3 | 4 |
| 5 | 6 | 7 | 8 | 9 | 10 | 11 |
| 12 | 13 | 14 | 15 | 16 | 17 | 18 |
| 19 | 20 | 21 | 22 | 23 | 24 | 25 |
| 26 | 27 | 28 | 29 | 30 |   |   |

## MAY
| M | T | W | T | F | S | S |
|---|---|---|---|---|---|---|
|   |   |   |   |   | 1 | 2 |
| 3 | 4 | 5 | 6 | 7 | 8 | 9 |
| 10 | 11 | 12 | 13 | 14 | 15 | 16 |
| 17 | 18 | 19 | 20 | 21 | 22 | 23 |
| 24 | 25 | 26 | 27 | 28 | 29 | 30 |
| 31 |   |   |   |   |   |   |

## JUNE
| M | T | W | T | F | S | S |
|---|---|---|---|---|---|---|
|   | 1 | 2 | 3 | 4 | 5 | 6 |
| 7 | 8 | 9 | 10 | 11 | 12 | 13 |
| 14 | 15 | 16 | 17 | 18 | 19 | 20 |
| 21 | 22 | 23 | 24 | 25 | 26 | 27 |
| 28 | 29 | 30 |   |   |   |   |

## JULY
| M | T | W | T | F | S | S |
|---|---|---|---|---|---|---|
|   |   |   | 1 | 2 | 3 | 4 |
| 5 | 6 | 7 | 8 | 9 | 10 | 11 |
| 12 | 13 | 14 | 15 | 16 | 17 | 18 |
| 19 | 20 | 21 | 22 | 23 | 24 | 25 |
| 26 | 27 | 28 | 29 | 30 | 31 |   |

## AUGUST
| M | T | W | T | F | S | S |
|---|---|---|---|---|---|---|
|   |   |   |   |   |   | 1 |
| 2 | 3 | 4 | 5 | 6 | 7 | 8 |
| 9 | 10 | 11 | 12 | 13 | 14 | 15 |
| 16 | 17 | 18 | 19 | 20 | 21 | 22 |
| 23 | 24 | 25 | 26 | 27 | 28 | 29 |
| 30 | 31 |   |   |   |   |   |

## SEPTEMBER
| M | T | W | T | F | S | S |
|---|---|---|---|---|---|---|
|   |   | 1 | 2 | 3 | 4 | 5 |
| 6 | 7 | 8 | 9 | 10 | 11 | 12 |
| 13 | 14 | 15 | 16 | 17 | 18 | 19 |
| 20 | 21 | 22 | 23 | 24 | 25 | 26 |
| 27 | 28 | 29 | 30 |   |   |   |

## OCTOBER
| M | T | W | T | F | S | S |
|---|---|---|---|---|---|---|
|   |   |   |   | 1 | 2 | 3 |
| 4 | 5 | 6 | 7 | 8 | 9 | 10 |
| 11 | 12 | 13 | 14 | 15 | 16 | 17 |
| 18 | 19 | 20 | 21 | 22 | 23 | 24 |
| 25 | 26 | 27 | 28 | 29 | 30 | 31 |

## NOVEMBER
| M | T | W | T | F | S | S |
|---|---|---|---|---|---|---|
| 1 | 2 | 3 | 4 | 5 | 6 | 7 |
| 8 | 9 | 10 | 11 | 12 | 13 | 14 |
| 15 | 16 | 17 | 18 | 19 | 20 | 21 |
| 22 | 23 | 24 | 25 | 26 | 27 | 28 |
| 29 | 30 |   |   |   |   |   |

## DECEMBER
| M | T | W | T | F | S | S |
|---|---|---|---|---|---|---|
|   |   | 1 | 2 | 3 | 4 | 5 |
| 6 | 7 | 8 | 9 | 10 | 11 | 12 |
| 13 | 14 | 15 | 16 | 17 | 18 | 19 |
| 20 | 21 | 22 | 23 | 24 | 25 | 26 |
| 27 | 28 | 29 | 30 | 31 |   |   |

# 2000

## JANUARY
| M | T | W | T | F | S | S |
|---|---|---|---|---|---|---|
|   |   |   |   |   | 1 | 2 |
| 3 | 4 | 5 | 6 | 7 | 8 | 9 |
| 10 | 11 | 12 | 13 | 14 | 15 | 16 |
| 17 | 18 | 19 | 20 | 21 | 22 | 23 |
| 24 | 25 | 26 | 27 | 28 | 29 | 30 |
| 31 |   |   |   |   |   |   |

## FEBRUARY
| M | T | W | T | F | S | S |
|---|---|---|---|---|---|---|
|   | 1 | 2 | 3 | 4 | 5 | 6 |
| 7 | 8 | 9 | 10 | 11 | 12 | 13 |
| 14 | 15 | 16 | 17 | 18 | 19 | 20 |
| 21 | 22 | 23 | 24 | 25 | 26 | 27 |
| 28 | 29 |   |   |   |   |   |

## MARCH
| M | T | W | T | F | S | S |
|---|---|---|---|---|---|---|
|   |   | 1 | 2 | 3 | 4 | 5 |
| 6 | 7 | 8 | 9 | 10 | 11 | 12 |
| 13 | 14 | 15 | 16 | 17 | 18 | 19 |
| 20 | 21 | 22 | 23 | 24 | 25 | 26 |
| 27 | 28 | 29 | 30 | 31 |   |   |

## APRIL
| M | T | W | T | F | S | S |
|---|---|---|---|---|---|---|
|   |   |   |   |   | 1 | 2 |
| 3 | 4 | 5 | 6 | 7 | 8 | 9 |
| 10 | 11 | 12 | 13 | 14 | 15 | 16 |
| 17 | 18 | 19 | 20 | 21 | 22 | 23 |
| 24 | 25 | 26 | 27 | 28 | 29 | 30 |

## MAY
| M | T | W | T | F | S | S |
|---|---|---|---|---|---|---|
| 1 | 2 | 3 | 4 | 5 | 6 | 7 |
| 8 | 9 | 10 | 11 | 12 | 13 | 14 |
| 15 | 16 | 17 | 18 | 19 | 20 | 21 |
| 22 | 23 | 24 | 25 | 26 | 27 | 28 |
| 29 | 30 | 31 |   |   |   |   |

## JUNE
| M | T | W | T | F | S | S |
|---|---|---|---|---|---|---|
|   |   |   | 1 | 2 | 3 | 4 |
| 5 | 6 | 7 | 8 | 9 | 10 | 11 |
| 12 | 13 | 14 | 15 | 16 | 17 | 18 |
| 19 | 20 | 21 | 22 | 23 | 24 | 25 |
| 26 | 27 | 28 | 29 | 30 |   |   |

## JULY
| M | T | W | T | F | S | S |
|---|---|---|---|---|---|---|
|   |   |   |   |   | 1 | 2 |
| 3 | 4 | 5 | 6 | 7 | 8 | 9 |
| 10 | 11 | 12 | 13 | 14 | 15 | 16 |
| 17 | 18 | 19 | 20 | 21 | 22 | 23 |
| 24 | 25 | 26 | 27 | 28 | 29 | 30 |
| 31 |   |   |   |   |   |   |

## AUGUST
| M | T | W | T | F | S | S |
|---|---|---|---|---|---|---|
|   | 1 | 2 | 3 | 4 | 5 | 6 |
| 7 | 8 | 9 | 10 | 11 | 12 | 13 |
| 14 | 15 | 16 | 17 | 18 | 19 | 20 |
| 21 | 22 | 23 | 24 | 25 | 26 | 27 |
| 28 | 29 | 30 | 31 |   |   |   |

## SEPTEMBER
| M | T | W | T | F | S | S |
|---|---|---|---|---|---|---|
|   |   |   |   | 1 | 2 | 3 |
| 4 | 5 | 6 | 7 | 8 | 9 | 10 |
| 11 | 12 | 13 | 14 | 15 | 16 | 17 |
| 18 | 19 | 20 | 21 | 22 | 23 | 24 |
| 25 | 26 | 27 | 28 | 29 | 30 |   |

## OCTOBER
| M | T | W | T | F | S | S |
|---|---|---|---|---|---|---|
|   |   |   |   |   |   | 1 |
| 2 | 3 | 4 | 5 | 6 | 7 | 8 |
| 9 | 10 | 11 | 12 | 13 | 14 | 15 |
| 16 | 17 | 18 | 19 | 20 | 21 | 22 |
| 23 | 24 | 25 | 26 | 27 | 28 | 29 |
| 30 | 31 |   |   |   |   |   |

## NOVEMBER
| M | T | W | T | F | S | S |
|---|---|---|---|---|---|---|
|   |   | 1 | 2 | 3 | 4 | 5 |
| 6 | 7 | 8 | 9 | 10 | 11 | 12 |
| 13 | 14 | 15 | 16 | 17 | 18 | 19 |
| 20 | 21 | 22 | 23 | 24 | 25 | 26 |
| 27 | 28 | 29 | 30 |   |   |   |

## DECEMBER
| M | T | W | T | F | S | S |
|---|---|---|---|---|---|---|
|   |   |   |   | 1 | 2 | 3 |
| 4 | 5 | 6 | 7 | 8 | 9 | 10 |
| 11 | 12 | 13 | 14 | 15 | 16 | 17 |
| 18 | 19 | 20 | 21 | 22 | 23 | 24 |
| 25 | 26 | 27 | 28 | 29 | 30 | 31 |